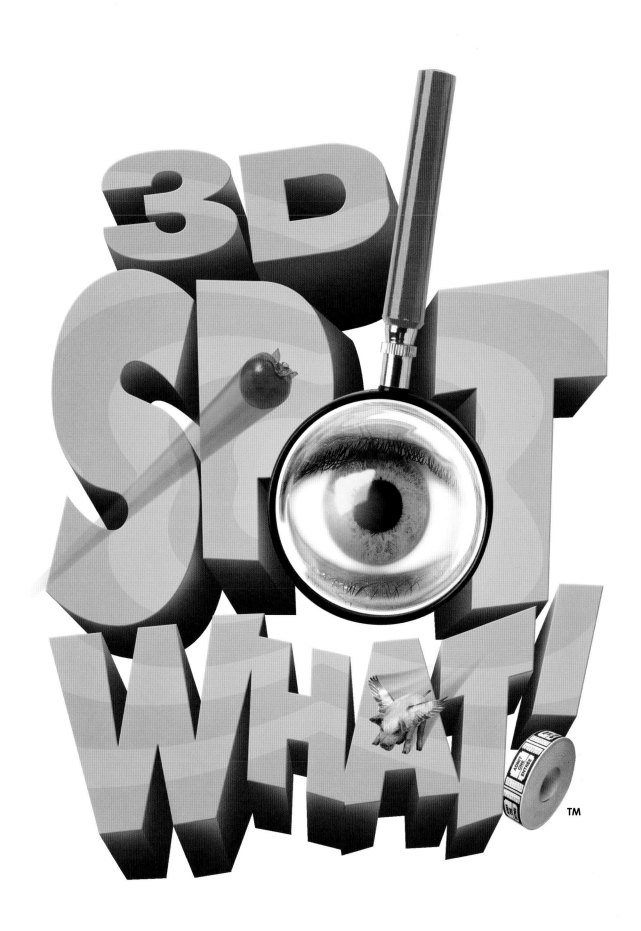

HINKLER BOOKS

Magic Mirror

Leprechaun

Court Jester

Created by Nick Bryant and Rowan Summers

Cover Design: Sonia Dixon
Prepress: Graphic Print Group
First published in 2006 by Hinkler Books Pty Ltd
45–55 Fairchild Street, Heatherton, Victoria, 3202, Australia
www.hinklerbooks.com

Copyright © Hinkler Books Pty Ltd 2006
First printed 2007

ISBN: 978-1-7415-7935-2

HB22_Apr10_06

Printed and bound in China

Binoculars

Dogfish

Accordion

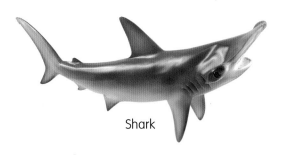

Shark

Viking Ship

Hourglass

Contents

Dinosaur

Parrot

Ice-cream Cart

Clown

Spot What Introduction

Welcome to **3D Spot What**!

Are you prepared to take the **Spot What** challenge? Can you find all the items cleverly hidden amongst the pages? Test your spotting skills and see how many you can find!

Each page has a list of items concealed within the images on the page. Work your way through the lists and see just how good a spotter you are!

You can take on the challenge by yourself, or you can battle against another person to see who is the ultimate spotting champion! On the next page we've provided the rules for the **Spot What** game and for the all-new **Spot What** sticker game.

Don't forget, a selection of the pages in this book are presented using amazing three-dimensional technology. Use the terrific 3D glasses that come with this book to give you a whole new dimension on the **Spot What** challenge!

Have fun, and good luck spotting!

Mask

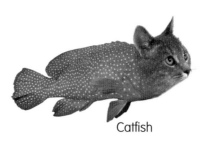

Catfish

Wizard

Rules for the Spot What Game

1. Flip a coin to see who goes first.

2. The winner of the coin toss chooses a picture from the book and then picks something for the other person to find, saying, for example, 'Can you spot a space ship?'

3. The spotter must then find the item.

4. If he or she can't spot it, the winner gets 5 points and shows him or her where it is.

5. Then the winner takes another turn and chooses an item for the other person to spot.

6. If the spotter can find the item, then he or she gets 5 points and now it's his or her turn.

7. The first to reach 30 points wins, but you could also set your own limit of 50 or even 100 points, or simply play best out of three.

You can also make the game more interesting by putting a time limit of one to three minutes on the search. Try making up your own games too!

Trombone

Viking Helmet

Scuba Diver

Rules for the Spot What Sticker Game

1. This is a game for two to four players.

2. Each player selects a different colored sticker sheet from the envelope attached to the inside back cover of the book.

3. The aim of the game is to find as many items as possible. Start of the top of the list and see who can find the first item. The person who finds the item attaches a colored sticker to it.

4. If there is more than one item to find per entry (for example, find three lizards), race to see who can find the most.

5. Work your way through the list of items until you reach the end of the list for that page.

6. Add up who has the most stickers on the page.

7. Continue on through the book. The winner is the person who has the highest total at the end of the game.

8. Alternatively, you can play by setting a time limit and seeing who can find the most items from the list before the time limit runs out. You could also try setting a limit of several minutes for one page, then reducing that by 20 seconds each page, until you reach the end of the book.

9. When you have finished the game, re-attach the stickers to the correct sticker sheets, keeping the colors in the right order. Store the stickers in the envelope at the back of the book until you're ready to play the **Spot What** sticker game again!

You can also use the stickers to play by yourself, so you can easily see which items you have found. Try timing yourself and see if you can beat your time on the next page! You can also set a time limit and see how many items you can find in that time.

Two elephants
One bat
One moose
Three giraffes
One tiger
One pussycat
One leopard
Three wise
  monkeys
One golden egg

One lion
One owl
Four eagles
Three dogs
One hippo
One sheep
One mouse
One rabbit
One goose

One frog
Three lizards
One early
  bird getting
  the worm
Two feathers
One spider
One fly
One snail

SPECTACULAR GORGE

One duck
One lost umbrella
One blimp
One squid
Three different hats
One witch
One kite
One pie in the sky
Three parachutes
One flying pig
One boomerang
Six balloons
One purple propeller
One bat
One butterfly
Four green leaves
Three hourglasses
One eagle
The world's first plane
One pair of socks
Two elastic bands

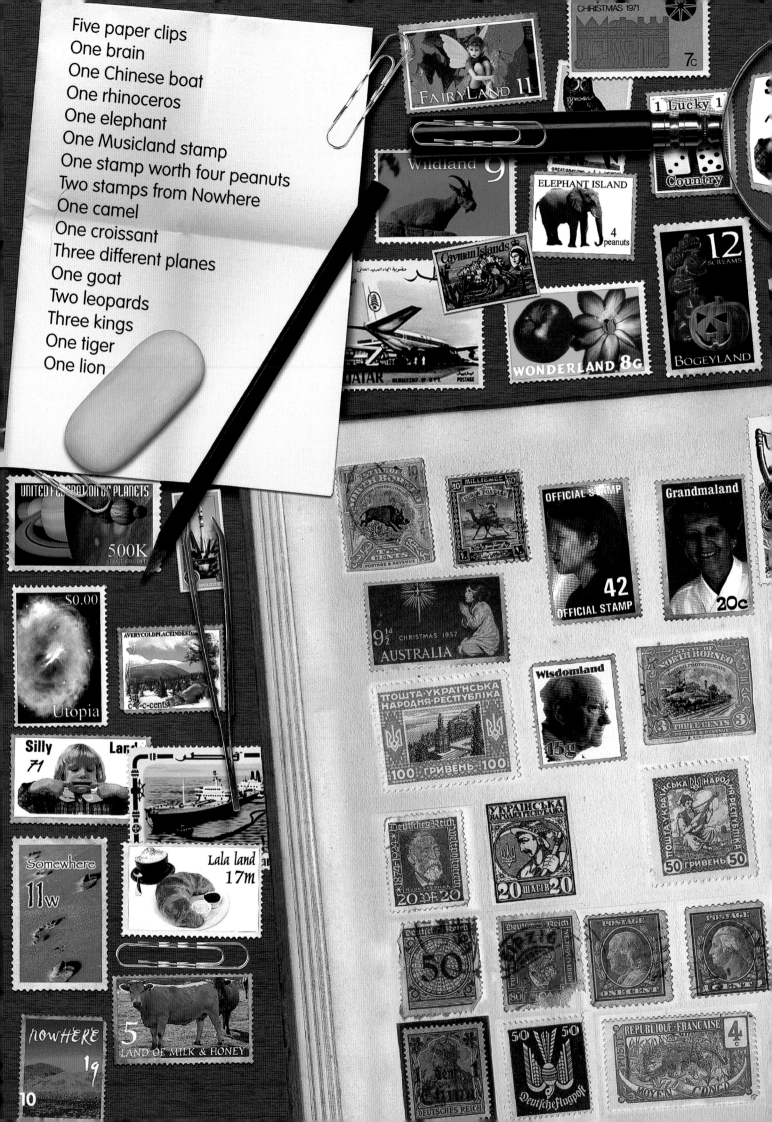

Five paper clips
One brain
One Chinese boat
One rhinoceros
One elephant
One Musicland stamp
One stamp worth four peanuts
Two stamps from Nowhere
One camel
One croissant
Three different planes
One goat
Two leopards
Three kings
One tiger
One lion

One leopard
One spear
One cow
One welcome mat
Two bulls
One baby bear
One vintage car
Five dinosaurs
One clock
One scoreboard
One moose

Three Ferris wheels
One sheep
One deer
Two stone cats
The words 'GO GO DANCE'
A path to spell 'AMAZING'
Two seals
Seven jacks
Five barrels
One Indian brave
One moon
Four shields

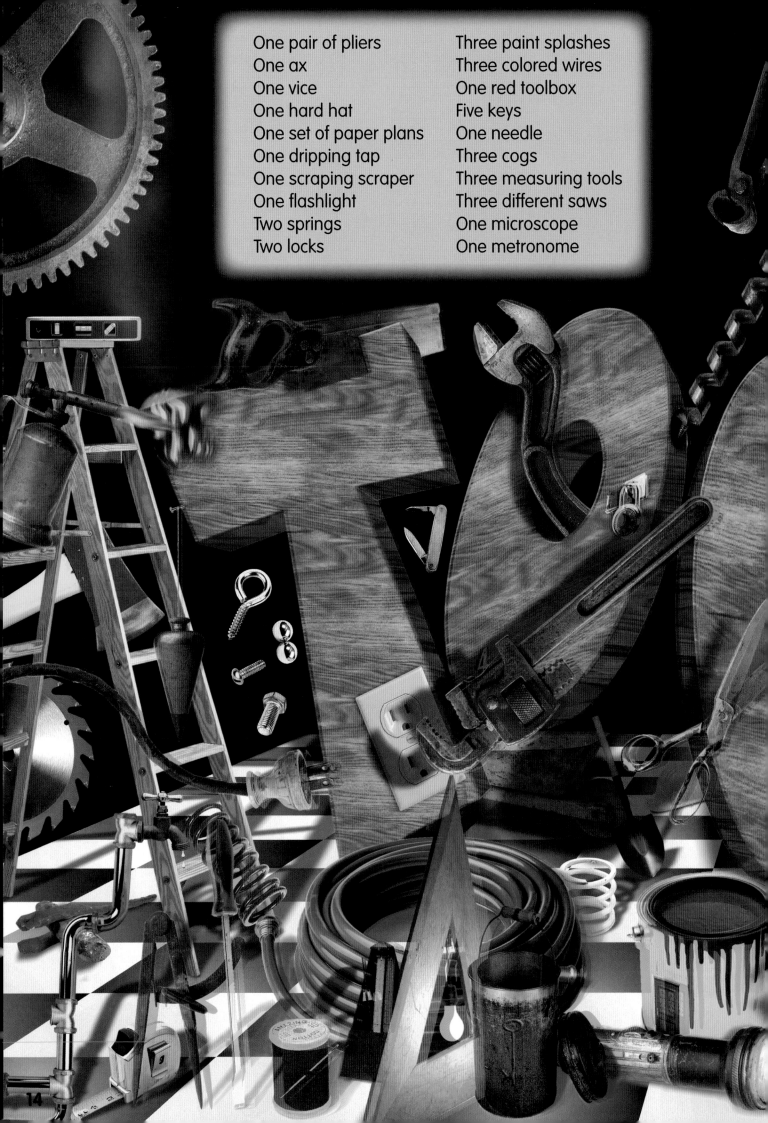

One pair of pliers
One ax
One vice
One hard hat
One set of paper plans
One dripping tap
One scraping scraper
One flashlight
Two springs
Two locks

Three paint splashes
Three colored wires
One red toolbox
Five keys
One needle
Three cogs
Three measuring tools
Three different saws
One microscope
One metronome

14

One jellyfish   Five leaping dolphins
Two skulls   One pair of oars
One turtle   One lighthouse
One catfish   One dogfish
One pearl   One treasure chest
One crab   Four starfish
One octopus   Four scuba divers
One coin   One seal
One kettle   Two anchors
Two seagulls   One message in a bottle
One door   Seven seashells
One seahorse

SS SPECTACULAR

AZZO

SLOW HALF FULL AHEAD STOP ASTERN SLOW HALF FULL

17

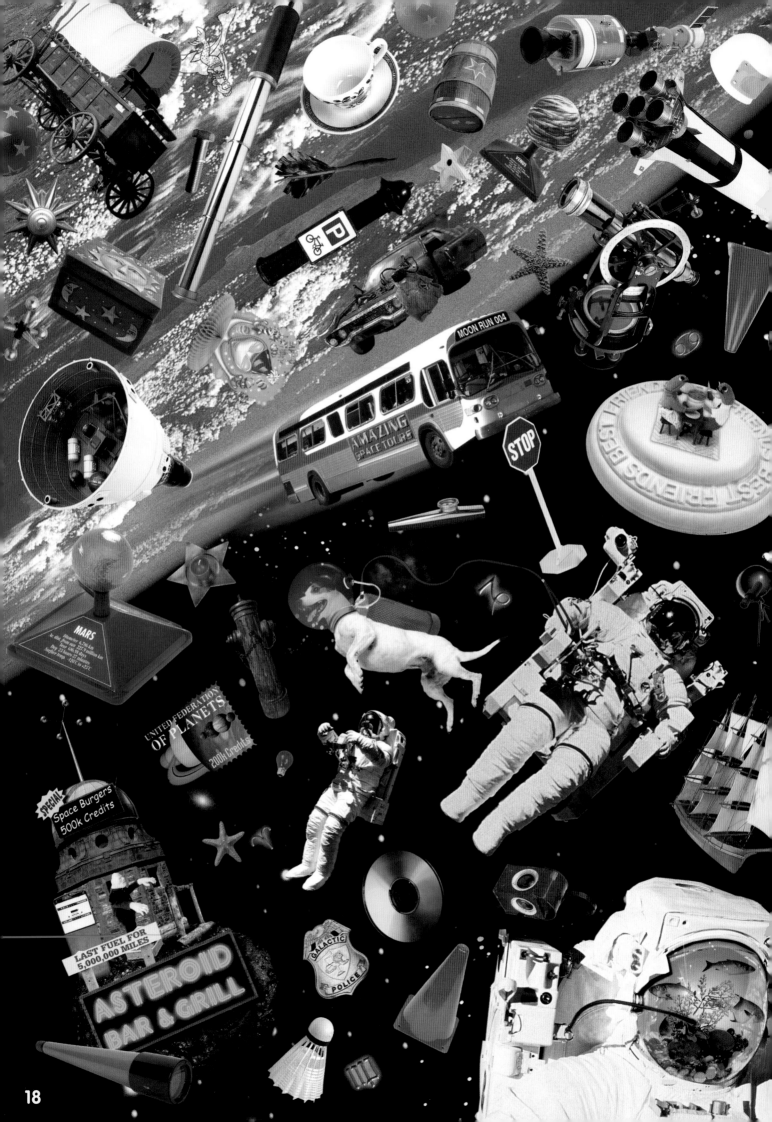

Four starfish
One magnet
One CD
One television
One sailing ship
One house
One chimpanzee
One barrel
One bottle
Five astronauts
One golf ball
One flying horse

One nut
One bolt
One satellite dish
One set of planetary rings
Twelve zodiac symbols
One parking meter
One picnic
One space shuttle
Four telescopes
Venus
Mars
One kazoo

One candy cane
One pair of pointy shoes
Two fours
One heart of gold
One peacock
One egg
The planet Earth
One clover
One car
One boat
One train
One plane

Three emus
One sleigh
Santa Claus
One winning hand
One bride and groom
Seven pots of gold
One pineapple
One arched window
Two Christmas trees
Three lemons

One apple core
One soda can
One avocado
One bunch of grapes
One cob of corn
Two hot dogs
One pizza
Three different cheeses
One gingerbread man

Four bees
Three balloons
Three chili peppers
One set of teeth
One halved tomato
One Christmas tree
Six blue candles
Six strawberries
One carrot

One onion
One horseshoe
One spoon
One quill
Four chess pieces
One harp
Three seashells
One dogfish
One brain
One fan
One mortar and pestle
One burning candle

One lamp
One bassoon
One centaur
The solar system
One chocolate frog
One goose
Two butterflies
One coffee mug
One umbrella

One candlestick
One gingerbread man
One alarm clock
One lion
One frog
One snail
One puppy dog's tail
One soldier
One iron
Five rubber ducks
Three mice

Three silver bells
Four cockle shells
One moon
One watering can
One heart
Six paper planes
One apple
One golden egg
One abacus
'FI-130'
One family

AMAZING FALLS ->

One kangaroo
Five daisies
One snake
One soccer ball
One pineapple
One hose
One spade
One squirrel
One shuttlecock
One gnome
Three fairies

One canary
Five pine cones
One rake
One spider
One owl
One hummingbird
One hungry bee
One nest
Two lizards
Seven snails

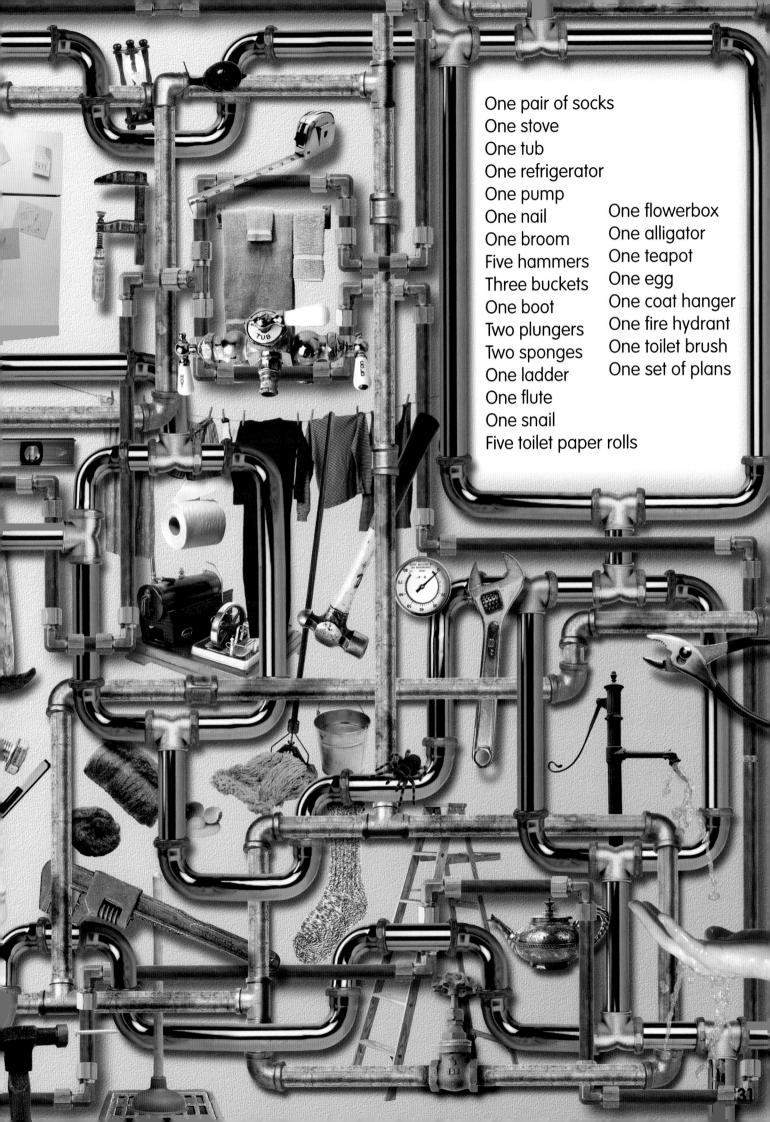

One pair of socks
One stove
One tub
One refrigerator
One pump
One nail
One broom
Five hammers
Three buckets
One boot
Two plungers
Two sponges
One ladder
One flute
One snail
Five toilet paper rolls

One flowerbox
One alligator
One teapot
One egg
One coat hanger
One fire hydrant
One toilet brush
One set of plans

DINGELING BROS.
CIRCUS

Roll Up! Roll Up!,
A spectacular to see,
The circus is in town,
Entertainment guaranteed!

Witness the high-flying
Fellini Brothers,
Perform death-defying,
Stupefying stunts above us,

With jugglers juggling,
Clowns clowning around,
The high wire dare-devils,
Dare-devillings astound,

A better time cannot
Be found anywhere,
So come on down,
To the Circus & Fair

Frank Flemming's
Fantastic
Flea Circus

KINDLY CONTROL YOURSELF

BALANCE

One juggler
Three acrobats
One balancing chair
Five stars
One trapeze artist
One merry-go-round
Two tightrope walkers
One apple
One pear
Three hoops
One tall hat

One unicyclist
One chimp
Seven clowns
Two photographers
Three noisemakers
Six umbrellas
Comedy and Tragedy
Two elephants
One snake
Two penguins

SPECTACULAR CIRCUS SIDESHOW ATTRACTIONS
& OTHERS
SWORD SWALLOWER
SMALLEST PERSON
10 TON
STRONG MAN
BEARDED LADY
RUBBER MAN
SIAMESE TWINS

EXIT

SPOT WHAT

POPCORN

ATTENTION

33

One jack-o'-lantern
Three balls
One dragon
Two lizards
One red wagon
One pair of gloves
Two orange boots
One frog
One car
One train
One cowboy

Three mice
Two cats
Four dogs
One wizard
Four dinosaurs
Twenty-three yellow stars
One elephant
Six musical instruments
One fairy
One green plane
Seven bears

POEM OF THE DAY

Fancy that,
A dancing cat,
To entertain the fans,

His only friend,
A singing hen,
Would clap if she had hands.

Benton Frappke December, 1908

One cotton reel
One plug
One caterpillar
One nib
One tag
One yacht
One dice
One bolt
One key
Three flies
One needle
Two centipedes

Two spiders
One ladybug
One hook
One nail
One gorilla
Butterfly A
Butterfly B
Butterfly C
One knight in armor
One pig
Four clown faces

To the Fellini Brothers,

One ball of wool
One pie
One fishing reel
One stapler
One fan
One egg
One frying pan
One candelabra
One knife
One banjo
One fork

One compass
One umbrella
One bow tie
One wagon wheel
One ship's wheel
One elephant
One gramophone
One fluffy bunny
One pair of ballet shoes
One guitar
One swan

Spectacular Flower Arrangements

10

One rhinoceros
One llama
One stork
One sheep dog
One shepherd
One big bad wolf
Three little pigs
One spinning wheel
One leopard
Three elephants
One camel

One dodo
One pitchfork
Three goats
One iguana
Rapunzel
Three kings
One rooster
One mousetrap
Quasimodo
One pocket watch
One pirate flag

Program

One purse	One doctor
One hen	One nurse
One fox	One snake
One snowflake	One pair of sunglasses
Two teapots	One soccer ball
One cowboy	One volley ball
One parrot	One football
One sleeping person	One tennis ball
One jack-in-the-box	Knitting
Six robots	
Three sheep	

One basketball
One tennis ball
One dart
Two bats
One jump rope
One bowling ball
One pair of ice skates
Two whistles
One stopwatch
One checkered flag

One saddle
One horse and cart
One fisherman's hat
One yo-yo
One hockey puck
Five soccer balls
One boomerang
Two catcher's mitts
Two pairs of binoculars
Two shuttlecocks

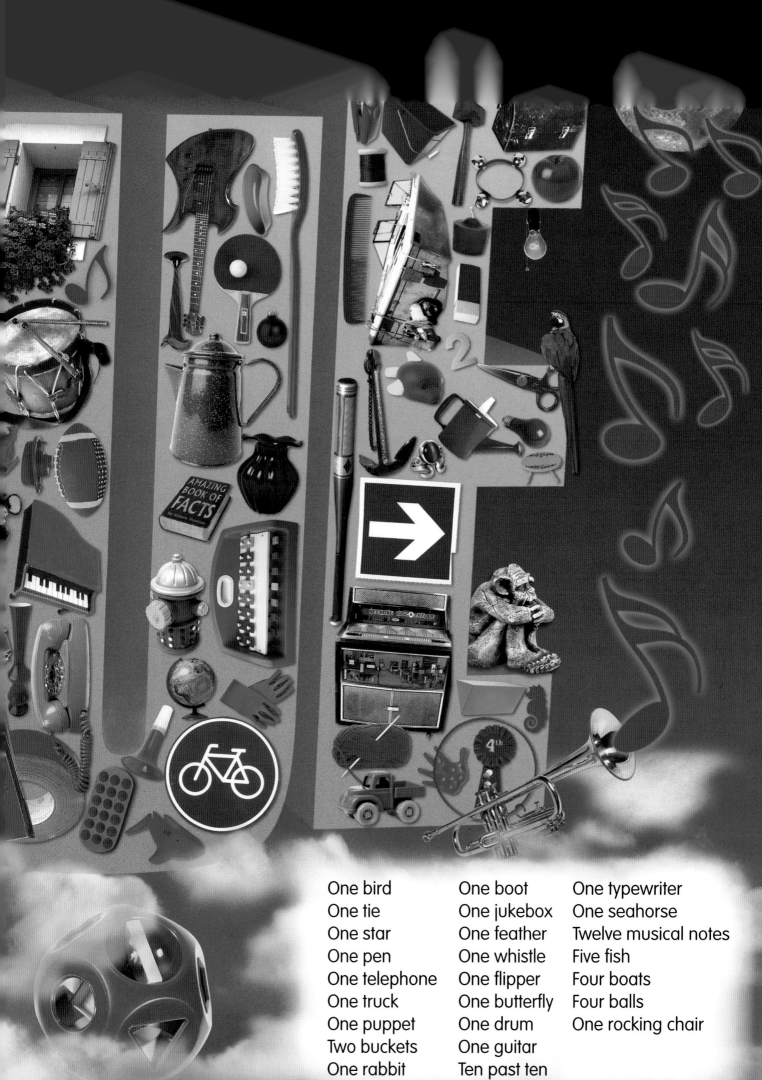

One bird
One tie
One star
One pen
One telephone
One truck
One puppet
Two buckets
One rabbit

One boot
One jukebox
One feather
One whistle
One flipper
One butterfly
One drum
One guitar
Ten past ten

One typewriter
One seahorse
Twelve musical notes
Five fish
Four boats
Four balls
One rocking chair

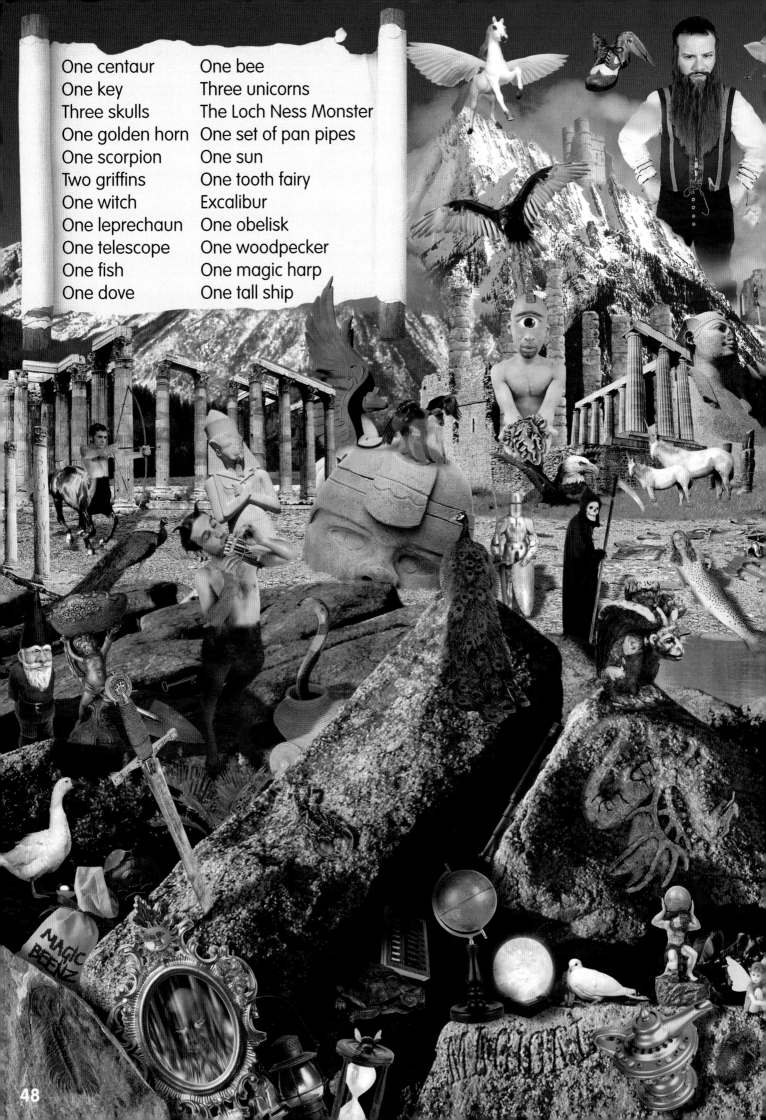

One centaur
One key
Three skulls
One golden horn
One scorpion
Two griffins
One witch
One leprechaun
One telescope
One fish
One dove

One bee
Three unicorns
The Loch Ness Monster
One set of pan pipes
One sun
One tooth fairy
Excalibur
One obelisk
One woodpecker
One magic harp
One tall ship

fountain of youth

MYTHS & LEGENDS

PROPERTY OF PANDORA

49

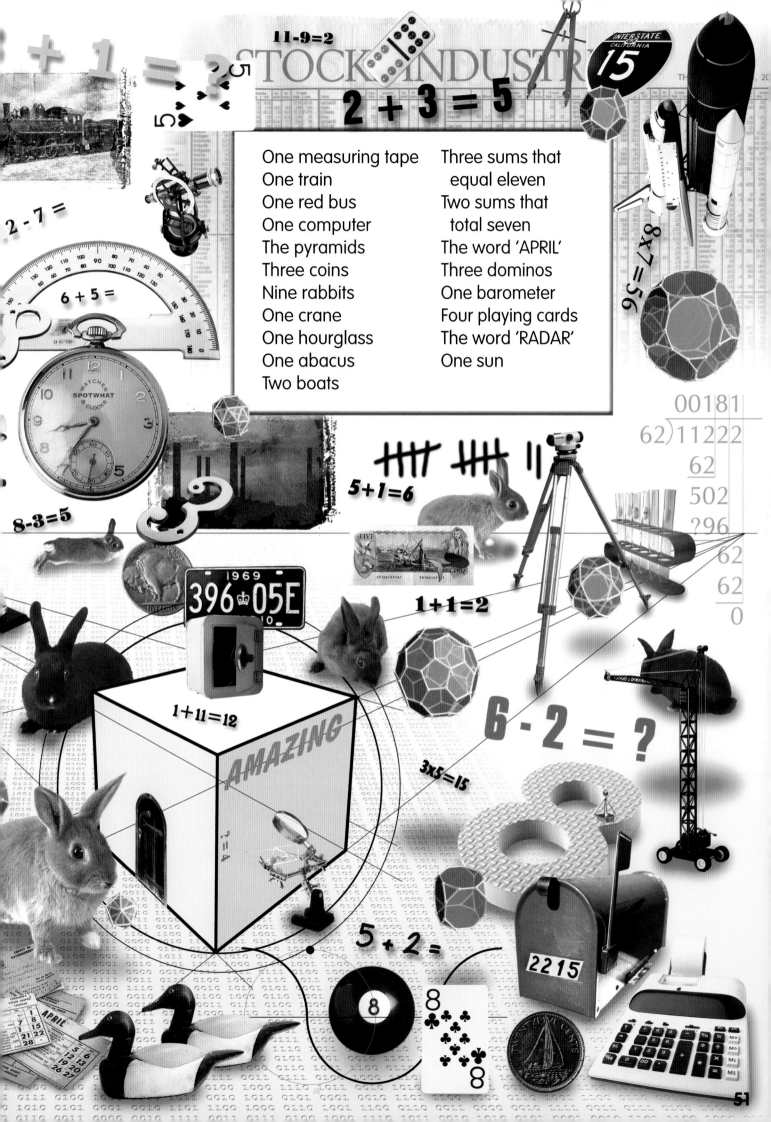

11-9=2

STOCK INDUSTR...

2 + 3 = 5

INTERSTATE CALIFORNIA 15

One measuring tape
One train
One red bus
One computer
The pyramids
Three coins
Nine rabbits
One crane
One hourglass
One abacus
Two boats

Three sums that
   equal eleven
Two sums that
   total seven
The word 'APRIL'
Three dominos
One barometer
Four playing cards
The word 'RADAR'
One sun

+ 1 = 25

2 - 7 =

6 + 5 =

8x7=56

8-3=5

5+1=6

1+1=2

1+11=12

6 - 2 = ?

3x5=15

?=4

AMAZING

5 + 2 =

1969 396 05E

2215

00181
62)11222
    62
    502
    ?96
    62
    62
    0

SPOTWHAT & CLOCKS

APRIL

51

One wishing well
One polar bear
One spoon
One dish
One parachute
One bird in a cage
One notebook
One witch
One worm
One cuckoo clock
Two rockets

One cello
Five yellow flowers
One blue balloon
One rocking chair
One kitten
One biplane
Mona Lisa
Time flies
East and west
Saturn
One butter churn

One watering can
Six insects
One Christmas tree
One parrot
One house
One lettuce
One olive
One chameleon
Two snakes
One four-leafed clover
One tyrannosaurus rex

One tractor
One horn
Three frogs
One pair of sunglasses
One carrot
One circuit board
One leprechaun
One Brussels sprout
One watermelon
One window
Ten green bottles

One car
One truck
One scorpion
One lizard
One duck
One windmill
One guitar
One match
One eggshell
One footprint
One statue

One astronaut
One skateboard
One blackboard
Ten gold bars
One surfboard
One wind-up mouse
One pair of scissors
One London bus
One Chinese checkers board
One jet plane

AUTOS WITH
TRAILERS
TRUCKS
55
MAXIMUM

RADAR
ENFORCED

12 ÷ 3 = ?

6 + 6

spot what

57

One wagon wheel
One skunk
One rooster
One raven
One pirate
Three apples
Two ghosts
One wheelbarrow
One invisible man
Two sacks
One ax
One hearse

One horse
One haunted house
One trunk
Three witches hats
Two candelabras
One oilcan
One cowardly lion
Three lanterns
Two pumpkin pies
Nine skulls
One headless horseman

SHEE'S APPLES

FUNERALS 'R' US

FOR SALE

RIP
IBBLES THE
GOLDFISH
1999 - 2000
ADLY WE SAY
GOODBVE TO
UR DEAR FISH

59

One set of keys
One red lipstick
Five rings
One band-aid
Seven coins
One pack of gum
Three brushes
One set of golden wings
One ticket to Wonderland

One set of lips
One candlestick
Five diamonds
One frog
One cat
One train
One umbrella
One pen

To you with love

Four guitars
One flute
Seven trumpets
One saxophone
One gramophone
One xylophone
One harp
One ukulele
Three stars

One clarinet
One lute
One banjo
One accordion
One pair of maracas
One bell
One tin whistle
One set of bongo
  drums

SPOT
WHAT

Napoleon
Two crowns
One lollipop
One flute
One camera
One daisy
One yo-yo
One watch
One puffin
One vase
One flashlight

One wand
Three clowns
One telephone
One tambourine
One squashed fruit
One flying machine
One saxophone
One set of keys
One penny farthing
One pen
One banana peel

FOR ONE
NIGHT ONLY

One bowler hat
One toaster
One eggbeater
Two chickens
One cherry
One piano
One bicycle
One pencil
One flipper
Two bubbles
One joker

One windmill
One zip
One rollercoaster
One domino
One boomerang
One canoe
One nut and bolt
One light bulb
One key
One eye spying

One key
One birthday cake
One telephone
One ring
One rattle
One thimble
One ladybug
One lobster
One eyeball
One skier
One ice cube
One log
One nest

One tree
One wing
One diamond
One rhinoceros
One light bulb
One fish bowl
Nine marbles
One mirror
One jack

Four cars
Two reindeer
Two penguins
One bear
One letterbox
Three pine cones
One fireplace
One snowman
One puppy
One sailboat
One dinosaur

Two tops
Two guitars
One chair
Two gingerbread men
Three snowflakes
Five sleds
One pogo stick
One woolly mitten
One birdhouse
One pair of spectacles

One gargoyle
One troll
One moose
Three mirrors
One gnome
One coin
One violin
One shuttlecock
One hourglass
Two swords
One pixie

One pyramid
One boat
One voodoo doll
One goose
One saw
One hammer
One pair of pliers
One clamp
Two axs
One dart
Three wands

One gingerbread man
One red bear
One chocolate éclair
One gum ball machine
Two strawberries
Two ice-cream cones
One car
One muffin
Four bananas

Two hearts
One green egg
One bite
Three buttons
Five bears in a row
Two red twists
The word 'HONEY'
Two lollipops
Nine balloons

Three radios
One spring
One lock
One paint brush
One icicle
Five vehicles
One kite
Five flowers
One ladybug
Three butterflies
One cactus

One clock
One reel of string
One bee
Five telephones
One ping-pong ball
Two pairs of scissors
One pair of gloves
Two snakes
Two drums
One funnel

One fisherman
One gnome
One dog
One peacock
One cat
One tower
One picnic
One dartboard
One television
One racing horse
One yellow window
One vintage car
One rabbit
One cow
One dolphin
Two merry-go-round horses
The words 'HOME SWEET HOME'

One frog
One rat
One gold teapot
One fork
One spanner
'OFLCTB'
The words 'THE END'

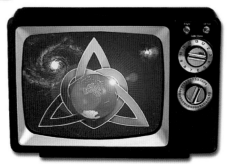

One clown
One pear
Four jacks
One thimble
One tomato face
One horse's head
One rocket ship
One owl
One path from A to B
One bear in a chair
One rainbow
Four barrels
The words 'SPOT THIS'
The words 'SPOT THAT'
One man with binoculars
Three horned helmets

spot what

spot this

SPOT THAT

Three dominos
Two giraffes
Three red dice
One blue dice
One pawn
One knight
One joker
Eight jacks
One queen
One king

One clown
One yo-yo
One fish bowl
One dog
Four flies
One thimble
One solitaire game
Fourteen marbles
One tic-tac-toe game
Two darts
One pig

Three arrows
One cat
One window full of clocks
One goldfish
Five lemons
One camera
One copy of this page
One ship
One giraffe
One 'FOR SALE' sign
Three candles
One mailbox
One baseball bat
Three shoes
Six ducks
One lantern
One scary smile
One bonsai garden
One mirror

TITANIC
SHIP OF DREAMS
ON HER MAIDEN VOYAGE
SOUTHAMPTON TO NEW YORK
APRIL 10, 1912

KINDLY CONTROL YOURSELF

GARAGE
TO LET

HORSE SHOE quality in Salmon
means that only the finest fish of
the catch are selected. That is the
reason for the appetizing, tasty,
delicious natural flavour, nutrition
and wholesomeness of

HORSE SHOE
SALMON

HEATED
APARTMENT
TO LET

Welcome

OFFICE HOURS
ON AND AFTER 12th MAY, 1919
BANKING HOURS WILL BE
10 a.m. — to — 2 p.m.
SATURDAYS
9 a.m. — to — 12 noon

Cropley's Attractive Footwear
FOR THE CHRISTMAS SEASON.

CROPLEYS LTD., GEORGE ST., HAYMARKET, & 600 GEORGE ST.

TELEPHONE

38

25¢
LEMONADE

FOR
SALE

One jack-in-the-box
One kite
One peacock
One dragon
One pirate
One rooster
One ship
One mermaid
One hummingbird
One harp
One unicorn
One bucking bronco

One grand piano
One name of a day
One knight
One wagon
One Pied Piper
One fish
One bow and arrow
One bridge
One fairy
One skipping girl
One court jester

One bus
One train
One monkey wrench
One jet
Six strawberries
One pair of lips
One ping pong ball
One toolbox
One Christmas hat
Two Christmas stockings
One tractor
One set of bolt cutters
One hardhat
One feather
One clamp
Two boxing gloves

The Bank of Smiles

The more you invest in life, the more you get back from it.

A smile costs nothing, but can mean so much.

To: Mother Hubbard
Address: The Shoe
Nursery Land

01/01/2000

SPOT WHA?

Account balance:

1/12/1999	Deposit	12 laughs
	Deposit	17 hugs
	Deposit	34 smiles
	Withdrawal	9 tears

y most beloved,

How happy I was to ... received your last letter.
... rvellous to read all a ... to th... d of ...
...nds very exciting. I ... this
...en raining here alm... the
...arden, but it does ma... to
I've heard that others are going to follow your ... to
Mr. Butcher, Mr. Baker and th... local Ca... don't kn...
all set off to sea in a _tub_ no less. ... re that ...
worthiness of such items but I'm ... as so
I'm sure you will be joining ...
... you very much and want ...
...earts.
All more lo...

Quan-Yin.

WITH
MY

Note

Shopping List:
4 x Bones for the dog.
2 x tins of dog food
1 x bottle of milk
1 Packet of dog biscuits
1 Bottle of dog shampoo
Flea Powder
hair brush

9th

One spider
One boat
One medal
One telephone
One turtle
One bicycle
One violin
One feather
One map
Three green tacks
Five kittens
One love note
Nine brass tacks
The words 'HAPPY BIRTHDAY'
One tic-tac-toe game
One piano player
One butterfly
One helicopter

One wooden plane
One sewing machine
One fluffy yellow duck
One house
One piano
One tractor
One tricycle
One windmill
Three horses
One tambourine

One carrot
One wind-up mouse
Two dinosaurs
One eggbeater
One hammer
One spanner
One lion
One purse
One cow jumping
over the moon

94

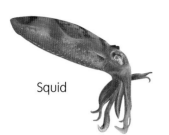
Squid

Pogo Stick

Hummingbird

Acknowledgements
We would like to thank the following people:

Sam Bryant
Suzanne Buckley
Sante Cigany
Claire Tennant
Dingeling Bros Circus
Samantha Boardman
Kendra Bishop
Derek Debenham
Rod and Mary Bryant
Louise Coulthard
Silvana Paolini
Stephen Ungar
Stephen Bishop
Kendra Bishop
Tracey Ahern

Sam Grimmer
Peter Wakeman
Peter Tovey Studios
Kate Bryant
Paul Scott
Tommy Z
Toby Bishop
Kristie Maxwell
Kelly-Anne Thompson
Miles Summers
Ruth Coleman
Heather Hammonds
Christopher Timms
Gillian Banham
Alison McDonald

Albert Meli from Continuous Recall
Qi Crystals Fossils Minerals, Melbourne, Vic
Little Ashlie, Michael, Nicole, and James for lending their toys
Everyone at Hinkler Books

Backgrounds for Gravity, Circus, Castle, Stage, Audience, and Emporium
by Stephen Evans s_evans42@yahoo.com
Furniture for 'Bedroom' created by Christopher Peregrine Timms
www. christophertimms.com.au
Thanks to Tsutomu Higo for the use of geometric models for 'Numbers'
www.asahi-net.or.jp/~nj2t-hg/

Knight in Armor

Genie

Robot

Cameo

Pumpkin Head

Turtle

Gorilla